Pictures and Memories

BABY'S FIRST YEAR

This book is about

_____

BRIMAX

Illustrated by Czes Pachela

HOW TO USE THIS BOOK

It's so easy to make your own unique, lasting record of Baby's first year. On each page there are special panels in which you can place photographs, postcards, gift paper, drawings, ribbons, tags – or anything you want to remind you of a treasured moment. You may wish to cut some pictures smaller to allow more to fit on the page or to make interesting shapes. Place a special picture of Baby on the first page in this book, and write his or her name beneath. Each page also has spaces for you to write in names, places, details of events and even your own thoughts.

First published in Great Britain in 2000 by Brimax
An imprint of Octopus Publishing Group Limited
2–4 Heron Quays, London, E14 4JP

This edition published in 2002 by Brimax

© Octopus Publishing Group Limited

Czes Pachela courtesy of Advocate, London

Created by Derek Hall & Associates
Designed by Kit Johnson

Printed in China

CONTENTS

BEFORE BABY ARRIVED

BABY'S FIRST DAY

BABY'S FIRST DAY HOME

BABY'S EARLY DAYS

BABY'S FIRST DAY OUT

NAMING BABY

BABY'S BATHTIME

BABY'S BEDROOM

BABY'S PLAYTIME

BABY'S FIRST HOLIDAY

BABY'S BIG MOMENTS

HAPPY BIRTHDAY, BABY!

BABY'S WELL-BEING

BEFORE BABY ARRIVED

BABY'S FAMILY TREE

Mother's side   *Father's side*

Great Grandparents   *Great Grandparents*

_____   _____

_____   _____

_____   _____

_____   _____

Grandparents   *Grandparents*

_____   _____

_____   _____

_____ *Mother*   *Father* _____

Baby's brothers and sisters

_____

Waiting for the great day

We first felt Baby move on ————————————

Baby was due to be born on ————————————

Names we considered for Baby

We attended prenatal classes at

————————————————

————————————————

————————————————

BABY'S FIRST DAY

Baby was born at _____

_____

The date and time were _____

The midwife and doctor were

_____

_____

_____

Present at the birth were _____

Baby weighed _____

Baby's length was _____

Our feelings were _____

Baby's eyes were _____

_____

Baby's hair was _____

Those first special moments

BABY'S FIRST DAY HOME

Baby came home on _____

We lived at _____

_____

_____

Baby wore _____

_____

Memories of a happy homecoming

We celebrated by

_____

_____

_____

_____

Baby was welcomed by

_____

_____

_____

_____

... and they brought these gifts _____

_____

BABY'S EARLY DAYS

Baby's feeding times were —————————

——————————————————

——————————————

Baby slept —————————

——————————————

... and woke —————————

——————————————

A new member of the family

Baby stopped crying when _____

_____

_____

Baby's first toys were _____

_____

Baby's first visitors were

_____

_____

_____

BABY'S FIRST DAY OUT

Baby's first day out was on _____

We went to _____

_____

_____

We went by _____

_____

Baby's first look at the big wide world

Baby wore _____

_____

_____

When we were there, we

_____

_____

This is who came, too! _____

_____

NAMING BABY

A very
special day
for Baby

Baby's name is _____

This name means _____

... and we chose it because _____

The christening or naming ceremony was held on _____

at _____

and was performed by

_____

Baby's godparents were

_____

_____

_____

_____

... and they gave these gifts

_____

_____

_____

BABY'S BATHTIME

Baby was bathed by

_____

_____

Baby's first big bath was on

_____

Baby's first bath at home was on

_____

… and Baby's bathtime was at

_____

… and these toys joined in!

_____

_____

The best thing about bathtime was

_____

_____

_____

*Bathtime fun …
what a splash!*

… but Baby didn't like

_____

_____

_____

BABY'S BEDROOM

Baby's bedroom was decorated with

_____

_____

_____

Baby's best bedtime toys were

_____

_____

… and best bedtime story was

_____

_____

Baby's own special place

The best way to get Baby to sleep was to _____

_____

... until Baby needed feeding at

_____

Baby first slept through the night on

_____

BABY'S PLAYTIME

Baby's best cuddly toy was _____

    ... but Baby also liked _____

    _____

    _____

Playtime is fun time!

Baby liked to play _____

_____

_____

... and this is who played, too! _____

Baby's best friend was _____

Baby's best book was _____

_____

BABY'S FIRST HOLIDAY

We went to _____

We went by _____   *This is who came along, too!*

_____

_____

_____

Baby's first
holiday postcard

... and so did Baby's best toys

_____

_____

_____

Baby liked _____

_____

_____

... but didn't like _____

_____

_____

BABY'S BIG MOMENTS

These are the dates Baby first ...

smiled _____   crawled _____

held head up _____   stood up _____

sat up _____   took a step _____

Baby's first words were

_____

These are the dates Baby first …

ate pureed food _____

ate solid food _____

used a cup _____

Baby's other big moments were _____

_____

just
take a look
at me!

HAPPY BIRTHDAY, BABY!

We celebrated Baby's first birthday at _____

_____

Baby wore _____

_____

First
birthday
memories

Also invited to Baby's party were

_____

_____

_____

Baby's best gifts were _____

_____

_____

We ate _____

_____

_____

... and drank _____

_____

_____

BABY'S WELL-BEING

Baby's doctor _____

Doctor's phone number _____

Baby's eyesight test date _____

Results _____

Baby's hearing test date _____

Results _____

Baby's blood group _____

Baby's vaccinations   Date

_____   _____

_____   _____

_____   _____

_____   _____

_____   _____

Baby's first tooth appeared on _____

... and Baby was made comfortable when teething by

_____

Special things to note _____

_____